SKYLANDERS

THE KAOS TRAP

Cover Artist: **Fico Ossio & David Garcia Cruz**
Collection Edits: **Justin Eisinger & Alonzo Simon**
Collection Designer: **Tom B. Long**
Bio designs by: **Sam Barlin**

HARDCOVER ISBN: 978-1-63140-141-1   SOFTCOVER ISBN: 978-1-63140-193-0   17 16 15 14   1 2 3 4

www.IDWPUBLISHING.com

Ted Adams, CEO & Publisher
Greg Goldstein, President & COO
Robbie Robbins, EVP/Sr. Graphic Artist
Chris Ryall, Chief Creative Officer/Editor-in-Chief
Matthew Ruzicka, CPA, Chief Financial Officer
Alan Payne, VP of Sales
Dirk Wood, VP of Marketing
Lorelei Bunjes, VP of Digital Services
Jeff Webber, VP of Digital Publishing & Business Development

Facebook: **facebook.com/idwpublishing**
Twitter: **@idwpublishing**
YouTube: **youtube.com/idwpublishing**
Instagram: **instagram.com/idwpublishing**
deviantART: **idwpublishing.deviantart.com**
Pinterest: **pinterest.com/idwpublishing/idw-staff-faves**

SKYLANDERS

THE KAOS TRAP

FORGETTING FLYNN

Story by:
RON MARZ and **DAVID A. RODRIGUEZ**
Art by:
MIKE BOWDEN
Colors by:
FERNANDO PENICHE

MINI BUT MIGHTY

Story by:
RON MARZ and **DAVID A. RODRIGUEZ**
Art by:
DAVID BALDEÓN
Colors by:
DAVID GARCIA CRUZ

WELCOME TO SKYLANDER ACADEMY

Story by:
RON MARZ and **DAVID A. RODRIGUEZ**
Art by:
FICO OSSIO
Colors by:
LEONARDO & ALICE ITO

THE TRAP MASTERS

Story by:
DAVID A. RODRIGUEZ, ALEX NESS and **MICHAEL GRAHAM**
Written by:
DAVID A. RODRIGUEZ
Art by:
MIKE BOWDEN
Colors by:
DAVID GARCIA CRUZ

Letters by:
DERON BENNETT & **TOM B. LONG**
Edited by:
DAVID HEDGECOCK

FORGETTING FLYNN

"...AND THE *GREATEST* PORTAL MASTER OF THEM ALL WAS *MASTER EON.*

"HE AND HIS SKYLANDERS PROTECTED THE MIGHTY *CORE OF LIGHT,* A DEVICE THAT NOT ONLY ENRICHED THE WORLD, BUT ALSO KEPT THE TERRIBLE *DARKNESS* AT BAY!

"THEN ONE DAY THE DARK PORTAL MASTER *KAOS* ARRIVED, AND UNLEASHED A FIERCE, POWERFUL BEAST CALLED THE *HYDRA.*

"THE SKYLANDERS FOUGHT BRAVELY, BUT THE HYDRA PROVED TOO STRONG...

"...AND *DESTROYED* THE CORE OF LIGHT!

"THE SKYLANDERS WERE CAUGHT IN THE CORE'S EXPLOSION, AND SENT ROCKETING AWAY FROM SKYLANDS, TOWARD A WORLD CALLED *EARTH.*

"SO FAR AWAY FROM THE *MAGIC* OF SKYLANDS, THE SKYLANDERS WERE ALMOST LIKE *TOYS...*

"...UNTIL A *NEW* GROUP OF PORTAL MASTERS FOUND THEM, AND HELPED THEM RETURN HOME TO PROTECT SKYLANDS FROM THE EVIL OF *KAOS!*

"BUT KAOS WOULDN'T BE DEFEATED SO *EASILY.* HE HATCHED A PLAN TO HARNESS THE POWER OF A LOST ARTIFACT CALLED THE *FIST OF ARKUS.*

"THAT WAS WHEN THE *FIRST* SKYLANDERS, THE *GIANTS,* RETURNED TO SKYLANDS, AND MADE *SHORT WORK* OF THE SHORT VILLAIN!

"SINCE THEN, *LOTS* MORE OF THE MISSING SKYLANDERS HAVE FOUND THEIR WAY HOME...

...INCLUDING THE AWESOME *SWAP FORCE* FROM THE CLOUDBREAK ISLANDS, HOME TO A VOLCANO OF *MAGIC.*

"THE SWAP FORCE STOPPED KAOS WHEN HE TRIED TO *EVILIZE* THE VOLCANO AND SPREAD *DARKNESS* THROUGHOUT SKYLANDS.

"AND NOW THE LEGENDARY SKYLAND WARRIORS THE *TRAP TEAM* ARE HERE, WITH THEIR AMAZING *TRAPTANIUM* WEAPONS.

"SOMEDAY, WEERUPTOR, *YOU'LL* BE A SKYLANDER JUST LIKE THEM, ..."

WELCOME TO SKYLANDER ACADEMY

WE'LL START WITH SOMETHING *VERY* SPECIAL. THIS *HUT* YOU SEE BEHIND ME...

...BELONGS TO *PERSEPHONE*. SHE CAN TRANSFORM GOLD INTO PURE MAGIC...

...AND YOU CAN USE MAGIC TO *UPGRADE* YOUR SKYLANDER ABILITIES.

COOL!

SHE'S SO *BEAUTIFUL!*

HEY, LADY!

OVER *HERE*, YOU'LL SEE ONE OF OUR *TRANSPORTER PADS*, WHICH CAN INSTANTLY SEND SKYLANDERS TO LOCATIONS ALL OVER SKYLANDER ACADEMY.

THAT'S *ZOO LOU!*

WELL, THAT *WAS* ZOO LOU.

NOW HE'S PROBABLY OFF ON SOME *EXCITING* ADVENTURE!

THE TRAP MASTERS

FOOD FIGHT

BIO

Food Fight does more than just play with his food, he battles with it! This tough little Veggie Warrior is the byproduct of a troll food experiment gone wrong. When the Troll Farmers Guild attempted to fertilize their soil with gunpowder, they got more than a super snack—they got an all-out Food Fight! Rising from the ground, he led the neighborhood Garden Patrol to victory. Later, he went on to defend his garden home against a rogue army of gnomes after they attempted to wrap the Asparagus people in bacon! His courage caught the eye of Master Eon, who decided that this was one veggie lover he needed on his side as a valued member of the Skylanders. When it comes to Food Fight, it's all you can eat for evil!

WILDFIRE

BIO

Wildfire was once a young lion of the Fire Claw Clan, about to enter into the Rite of Infernos—a test of survival in the treacherous fire plains. However, because he was made of gold, he was treated as an outcast and not allowed to participate. But this didn't stop him. That night, Wildfire secretly followed the path of the other lions, carrying only his father's enchanted shield. Soon he found them cornered by a giant flame scorpion. Using the shield, he protected the group from the beast's enormous stinging tail, giving them time to safely escape. And though Wildfire was injured in the fight, his father's shield magically changed him—magnifying the strength that was already in his heart—making him the mightiest of his clan. Now part of the Trap Team, Wildfire uses his enormous Traptanium-bonded shield to defend any and all who need it!

SNAP SHOT

BIO

Snap Shot came from a long line of Crocagators that lived in the remote Swamplands, where he hunted chompies for sport. After rounding up every evil critter in his homeland, Snap Shot ventured out into the world to learn new techniques that he could use to track down more challenging monsters. He journeyed far and wide, perfecting his archery skills with the Elves and his hunting skills with the wolves. Soon he was the most revered monster hunter in Skylands—a reputation that caught the attention of Master Eon. It then wasn't long before Snap Shot became the leader of the Trap Masters, a fearless team of Skylanders that mastered legendary weapons made of pure Traptanium. It was this elite team that tracked down and captured the most notorious villains Skylands had ever known!

WALLOP

BIO

For generations, *Wallop's* people used the volcanic lava pits of Mount Scorch to forge the most awesome weapons in all of Skylands. And Wallop was the finest apprentice any of the masters had ever seen. Using hammers in both of his mighty hands, he could tirelessly pound and shape the incredibly hot metal into the sharpest swords or the hardest axes. But on the day he was to demonstrate his skills to the masters of his craft, a fierce fire viper awoke from his deep sleep in the belly of the volcano. The huge snake erupted forth, attacking Wallop's village. But by bravely charging the beast with his two massive hammers, Wallop was able to bring down the creature and save his village. Now with his Traptanium-infused hammers, he fights with the Skylanders to protect the lands from any evil that rises to attack!

SKYLANDERS

FIND MORE SKYLANDERS™ COMICS

COMIC SHOP LOCATOR SERVICE
888-COMIC-BOOK
comicshoplocator.com

WWW.IDWPUBLISHING.COM